Garfield
by the
pound

BY: JIM DAVIS

BALLANTINE BOOKS · NEW YORK

Copyright © 1992 United Feature Syndicate, Inc.
GARFIELD Comic Strips: © 1990, 1991 United Feature
Syndicate, Inc.

All rights reserved under International and Pan-American
Copyright Conventions. Published in the United States
by Ballantine Books, a division of Random House, Inc.,
New York, and simultaneously in Canada by Random
House of Canada Limited, Toronto.

Library of Congress Catalog Card Number: 91-92161

ISBN: 0-345-37579-3

Manufactured in the United States of America

First Edition: March 1991

10 9 8 7 6 5 4 3 2 1

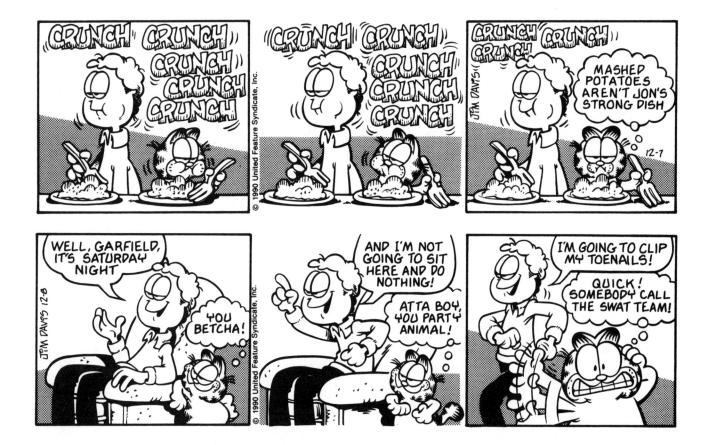

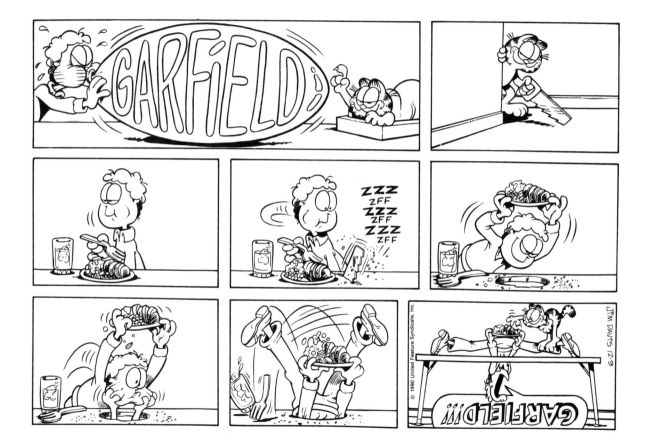

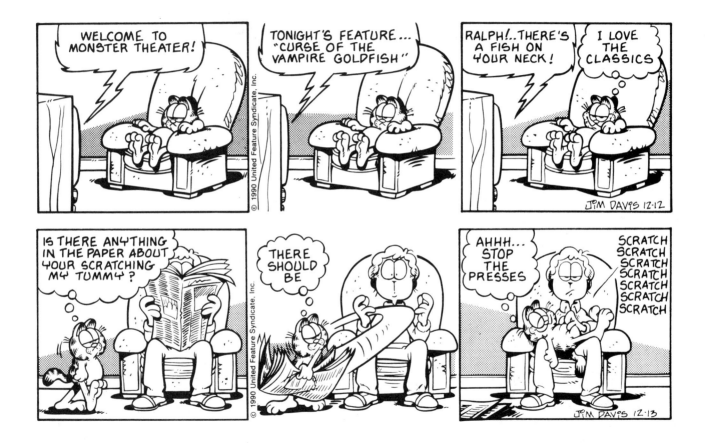

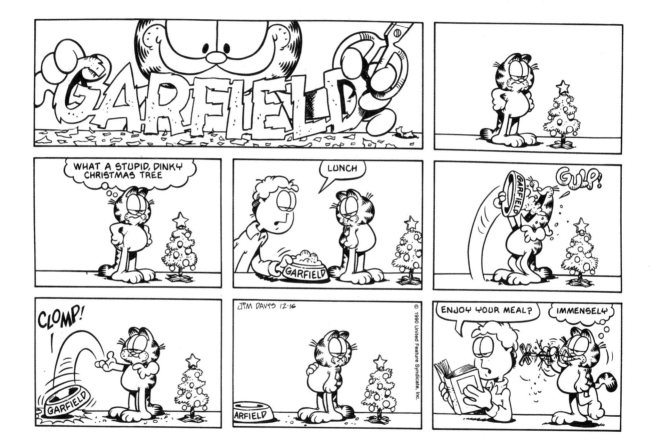

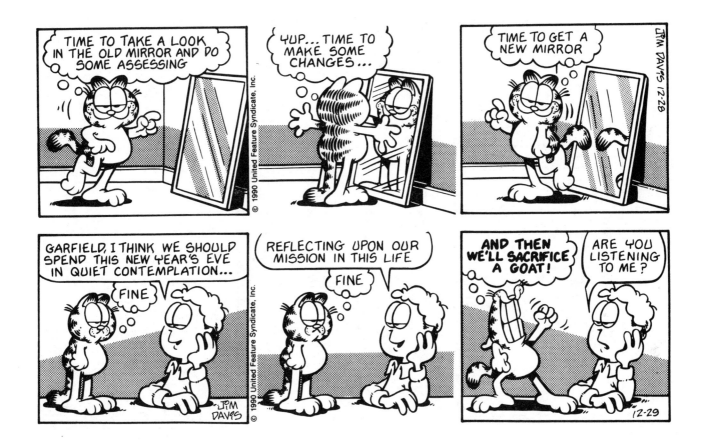

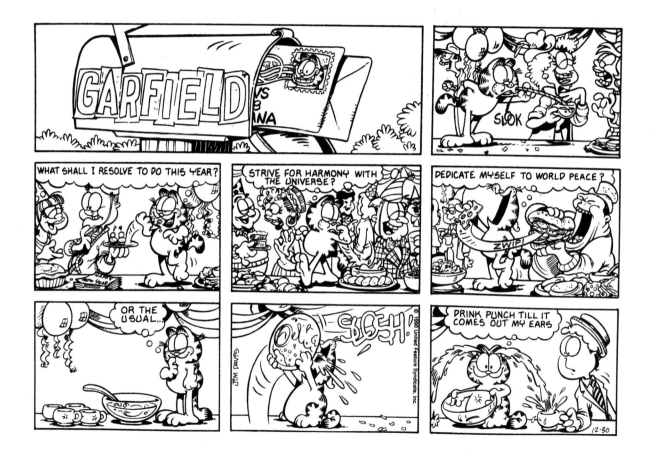

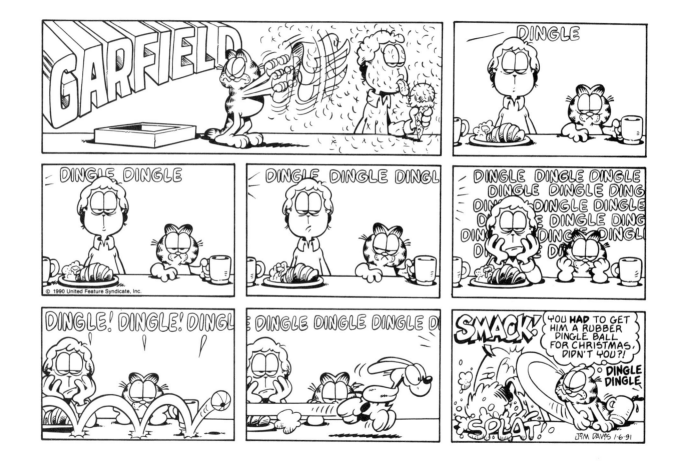

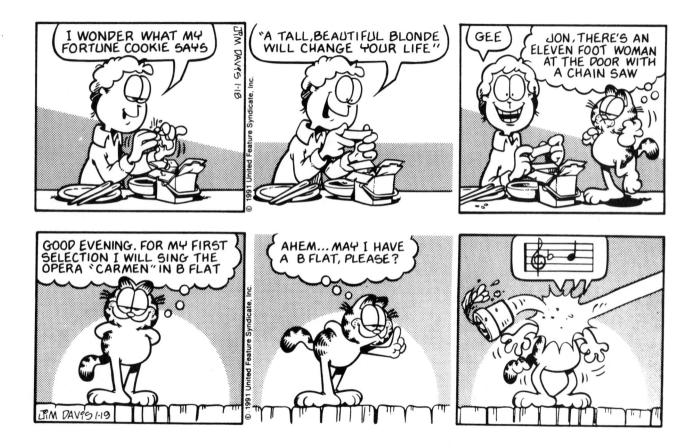

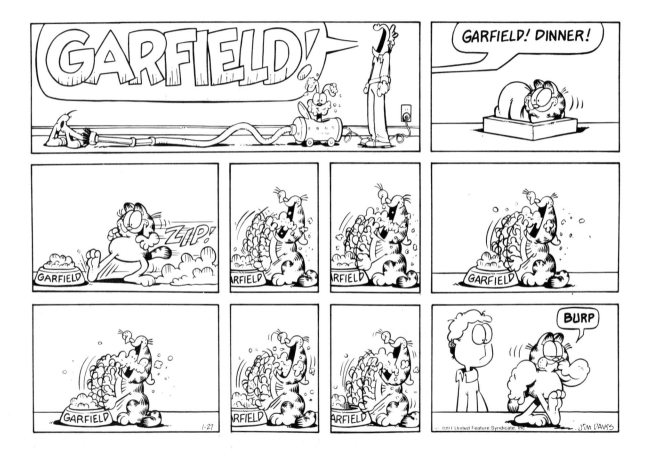

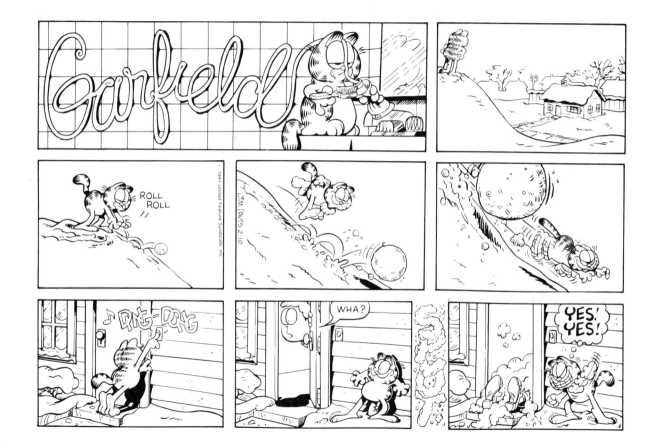

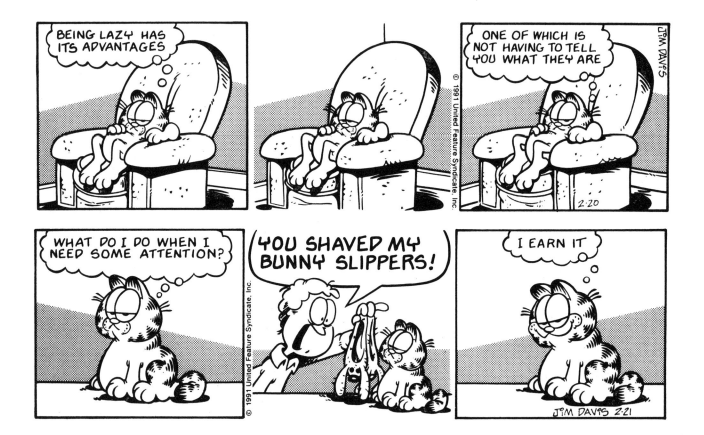

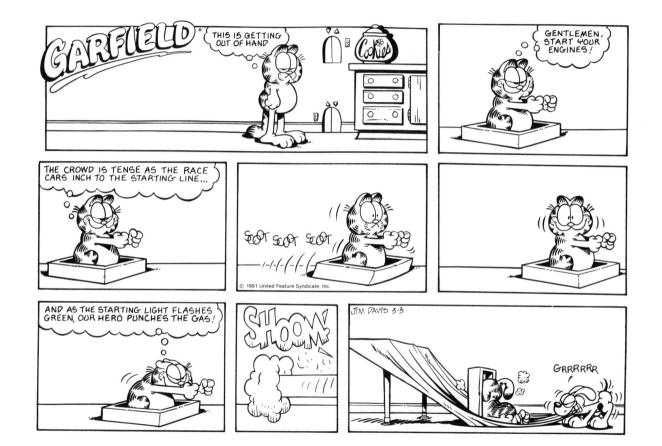

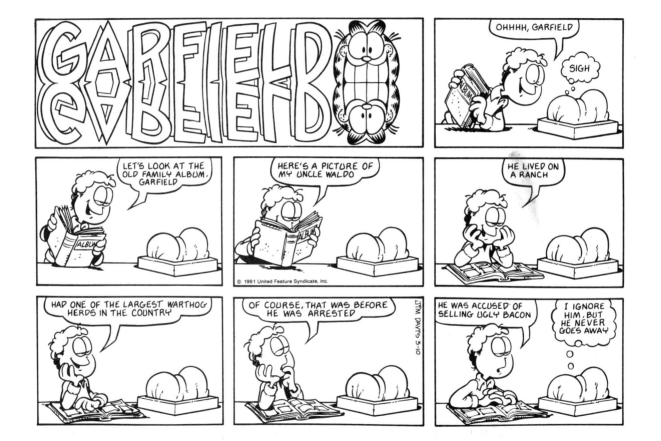

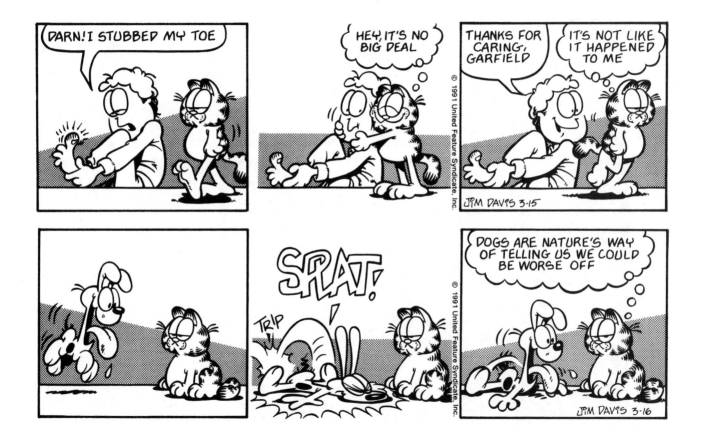

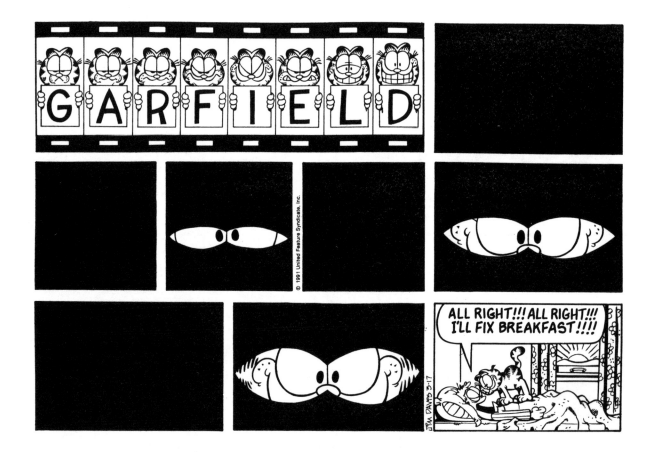

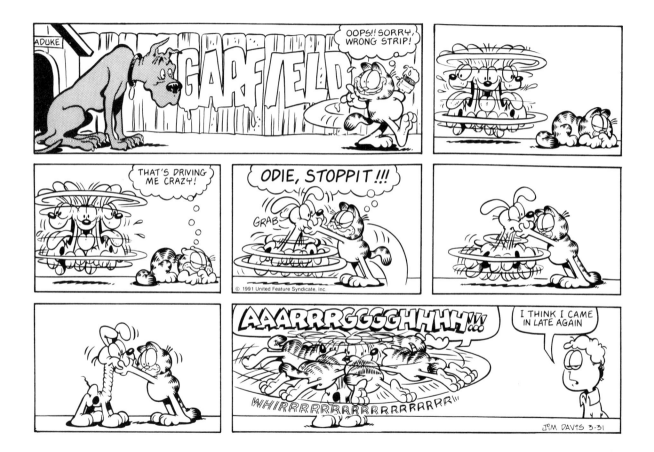

© 1991 United Feature Syndicate, Inc.

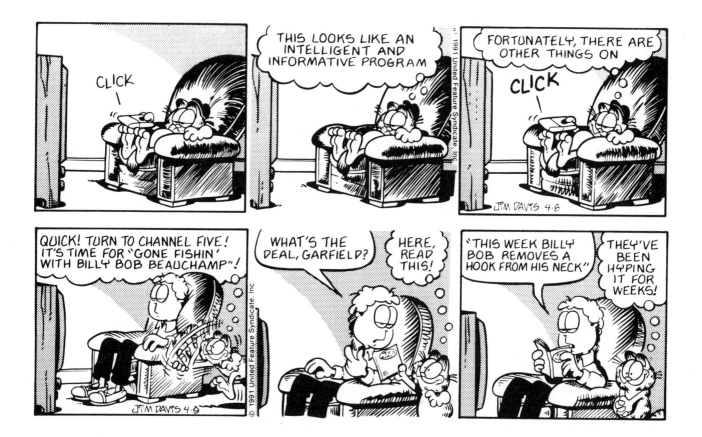

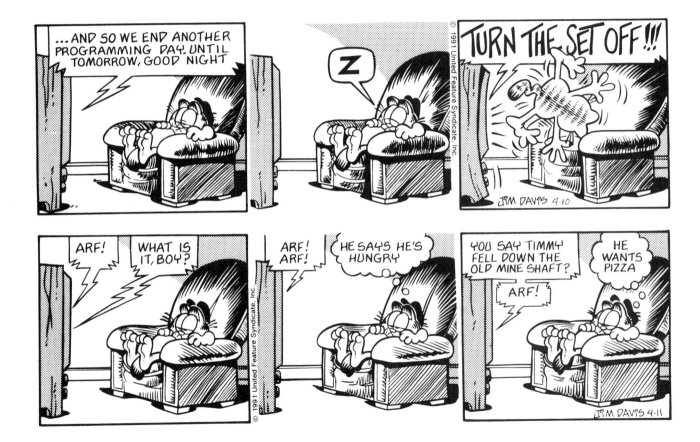

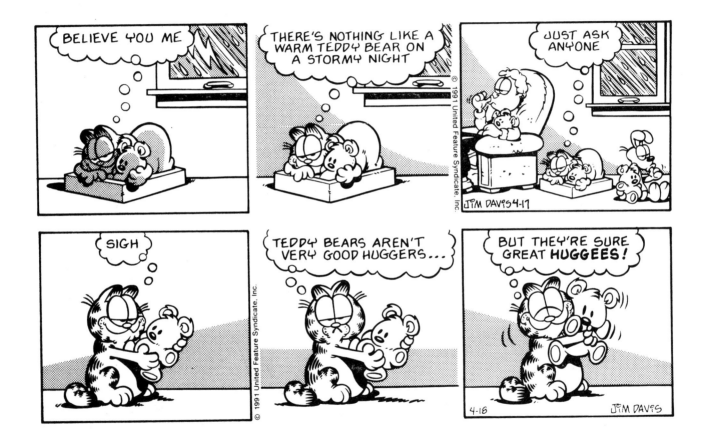

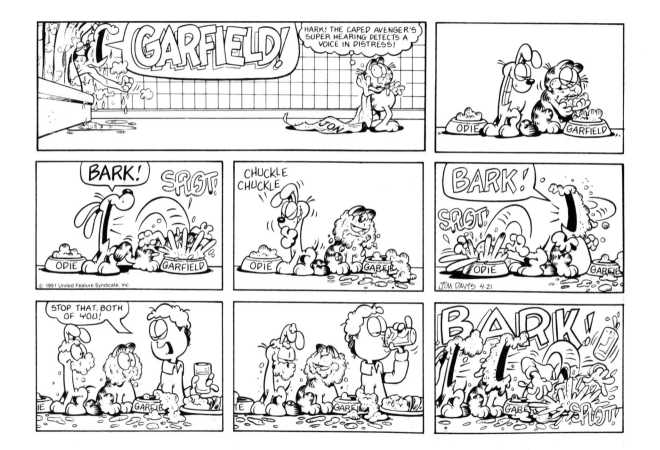

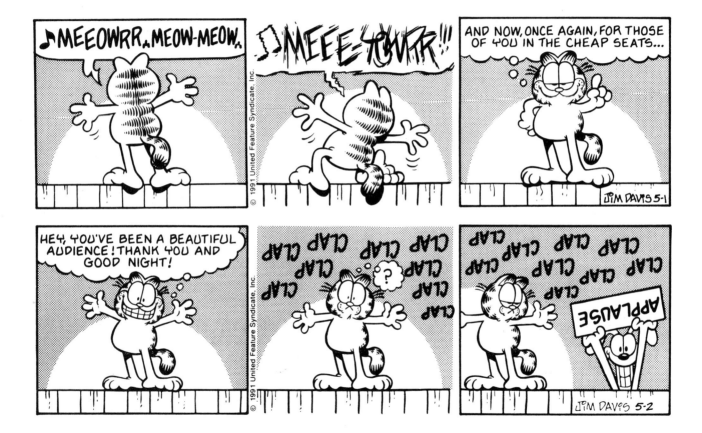

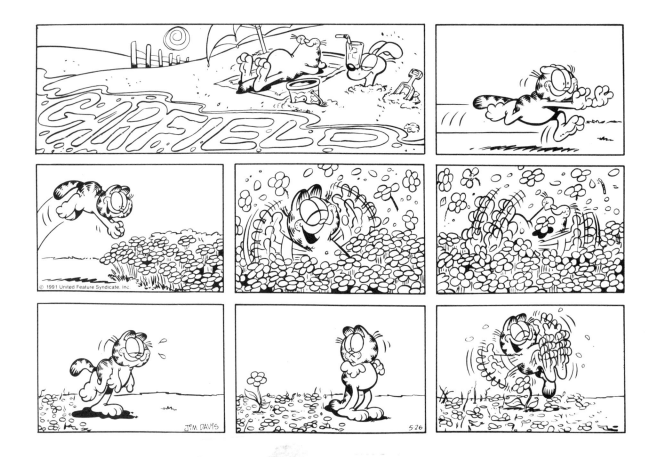

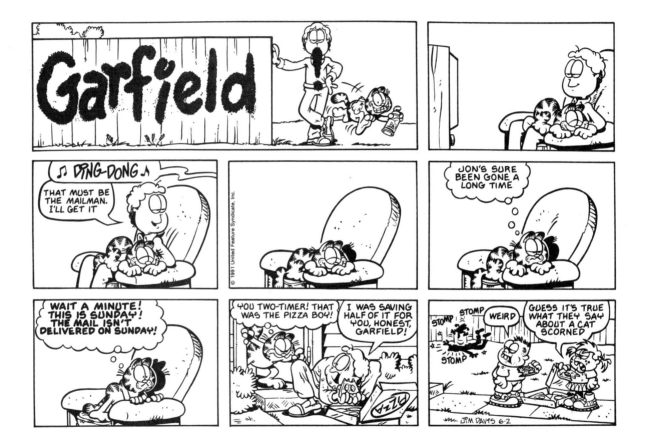

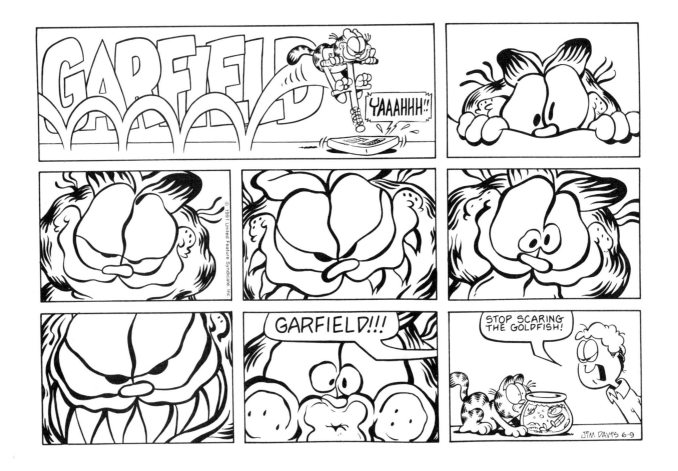

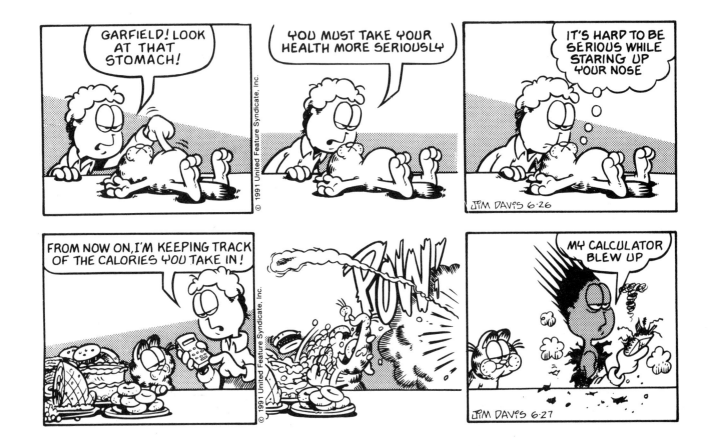

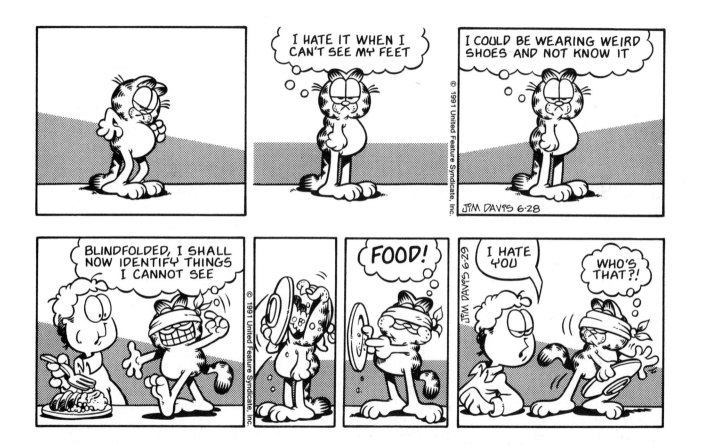

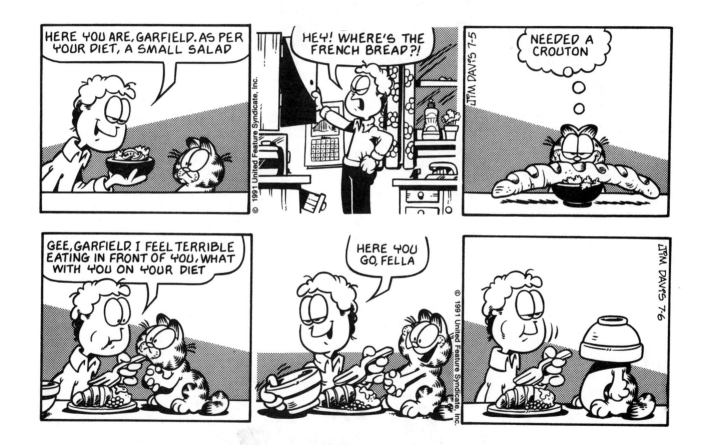

STRIPS, SPECIALS OR BESTSELLING BOOKS...
GARFIELD'S ON EVERYONE'S MENU

Don't miss even one episode in the Tubby Tabby's hilarious series!

___GARFIELD AT LARGE (#1)   32013/$6.95
___GARFIELD GAINS WEIGHT (#2)   32008/$6.95
___GARFIELD BIGGER THAN LIFE (#3)   32007/$6.95
___GARFIELD WEIGHS IN (#4)   32010/$6.95
___GARFIELD TAKES THE CAKE (#5)   32009/$6.95
___GARFIELD EATS HIS HEART OUT (#6)   32018/$6.95
___GARFIELD SITS AROUND THE HOUSE (#7)   32011/$6.95
___GARFIELD TIPS THE SCALE (#8)   33580/$6.95
___GARFIELD LOSES HIS FEET (#9)   31805/$6.95
___GARFIELD MAKES IT BIG (#10)   31928/$6.95
___GARFIELD ROLLS ON (#11)   32634/$6.95
___GARFIELD OUT TO LUNCH (#12)   33118/$6.95
___GARFIELD FOOD FOR THOUGHT (#13)   34129/$6.95

___GARFIELD SWALLOWS HIS PRIDE (#14)   34725/$6.95
___GARFIELD WORLDWIDE (#15)   35158/$6.95
___GARFIELD ROUNDS OUT (#16)   35388/$6.95
___GARFIELD CHEWS THE FAT (#17)   35956/$6.95
___GARFIELD GOES TO WAIST (#18)   36430/$6.95
___GARFIELD HANGS OUT (#19)   36835/$6.95
___GARFIELD TAKES UP SPACE (#20)   37029/$6.95
___GARFIELD SAYS A MOUTHFUL (#21)   37368/$6.95
___GARFIELD BY THE POUND (#22)   37579/$6.95

GARFIELD AT HIS SUNDAY BEST!
___GARFIELD TREASURY   33106/$9.95
___THE SECOND GARFIELD TREASURY   33276/$10.95
___THE THIRD GARFIELD TREASURY   32635/$9.95
___THE FOURTH GARFIELD TREASURY   34726/$10.95
___THE FIFTH GARFIELD TREASURY   36268/$9.95
___THE SIXTH GARFIELD TREASURY   37367/$10.95

BALLANTINE SALES
Dept. TA, 201 E. 50th St., New York, N.Y. 10022

Please send me the BALLANTINE BOOKS I have checked above. I am enclosing $ .... (add $2.00 for the first book and 50¢ for each additional book to cover postage and handling). Send check or money order—no cash or C.O.D.'s please. Prices are subject to change without notice.

Name _____

Address _____

City _____ State _____ Zip Code _____
30   Allow at least 4 weeks for delivery   3/90 TA-135

BIRTHDAYS, HOLIDAYS, OR ANY DAY...
Keep GARFIELD on your calendar all year 'round!